The Tradition of the Harvest

by Anne Sibley O'Brien
illustrated by John F. Martin

HOUGHTON MIFFLIN   BOSTON

Peter and his family sat around the table
at dinner. Peter looked at his plate of wild
rice and saw that each grain of rice had
split open. He ate some of the rice. It
had a nutty taste.

"Is it good?" asked his mother.

"It's better than good," said Peter.

The wild rice was *wonderful*. It was
also special to Peter because he had
helped pick it.

Every year, Peter's family went to the lake to pick, or *harvest*, the wild rice. This rice was a grain that grew wild in the water. The harvest was an important tradition for Peter's family. He and his family were Ojibwe (Oh-JIB-way), a Native-American people.

The Ojibwe had eaten wild rice for hundreds of years. The Ojibwe called the wild rice *manoomin*. They had learned that the rice could be made into good food.

4

Hundreds of years ago, the Ojibwe came to the Great Lakes in the northern part of the United States. Wild grass grew in the lakes, and the Ojibwe learned to harvest the seeds from the grass and cook them. They learned that the grass seeds were good to eat.

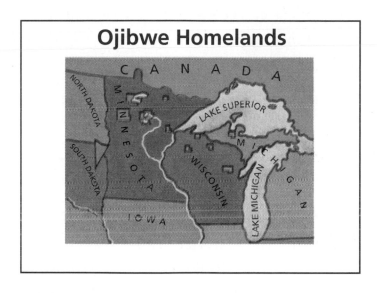

Ojibwe Homelands

When Ojibwe parents taught their children how to harvest the wild rice, they also told stories about a great hero called Manabozho (Man-a-BO-zo). Manabozho had helped his people find the lakes and the wild rice.

Today, many Ojibwe still live in the area near the lakes. Some Ojibwe, like Peter's family, still harvest the wild rice in the traditional way.

Autumn / Winter   **Spring**

Wild rice needs a year to grow. In autumn and winter, the wild rice seeds are in the mud under the water. In the spring, the melting snow brings floods. The seeds move in the water. Then they begin to grow roots. The roots grow into plants that reach for the sunlight.

By early summer, the plants grow above the water and begin to grow flowers. The plants grow taller and taller in the sun. By late summer, they are three feet above the water.

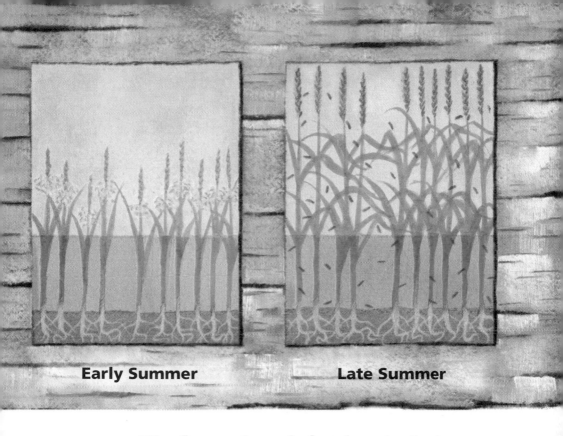

Early Summer   **Late Summer**

The flowers form dark red seeds. In August and September, these dark red seeds are ripe and begin to fall to the bottom of the lake. They will grow into grass the next spring.

The rest of the ripe seeds may be harvested before they can fall to the bottom of the lake.

In late August, Peter's family drove to the lake to harvest the rice. Peter looked out at the lake and through the tall grass. He saw a few ducks flying across the blue sky. They were enjoying the harvest too.

Peter's mother and grandfather took the canoe into the lake. Two people were needed to do the harvesting work. One person stood in the back of the canoe with a long pole. The pole was used to move the canoe through the water. The other person used two sticks to knock the grains of rice into the canoe.

Peter always came to the lake for the rice harvest. Until this year, he had spent the time there playing with his cousins.

On the third morning of harvesting, Peter woke up very early. The sun was just coming up. He dressed quickly. He was going to help with his first harvest. Today, he would work with his grandfather to harvest the rice. Peter went down to the lake.

Peter and his grandfather put the canoe into the water. Then they got into the canoe. Peter stood with the tall pole. His grandfather sat down in front of him.

"Now, push slowly," said Grandfather.

Peter put the pole into the mud and pushed. The canoe moved, but it also tipped to one side. Peter almost fell into the water. It was not easy to stand in a moving canoe.

The sun was hot and pushing with the pole was hard work. Soon Peter began to move the canoe well. Peter felt good that he could keep the canoe steady.

"Very good, Peter. You are doing well," Grandfather said. Grandfather held a stick in each hand and began to harvest the rice. Peter watched his grandfather use one stick to bend tall grass over the canoe. He hit the grass with the other stick so that most of the wild rice seeds fell into the canoe. Some of the seeds fell into the water. Next year, those seeds would grow into tall grass.

Again and again, Grandfather bent the tall grass over the canoe. He worked quickly as he hit the tops of the grass with the other stick. Peter listened to the sounds *swish, rap, swish, rap* as the pile of wild rice seed grew larger.

"Let's take a break," said Grandfather. Peter was happy to hear that because he was tired. They rested and talked. Then Peter and his grandfather traded places.

Peter tried to use the two sticks. The first time he hit the grass, most of the seeds fell into the water. A few hit his face. He kept trying, and he slowly improved.

Peter kept working. By noon, the canoe was full of wild rice. Peter and his grandfather then put the rice into bags and headed home. There were many more steps to "finish" the rice.

First, the family spread out the rice on
plastic sheets. The sun began to dry the rice.

Next, they put the rice in a big pot over a
fire where it dried more.

Then Grandfather "danced" on the rice.
As he danced, the rice husks, or outer shells,
broke away. The rice grains were inside.

Next, the wild rice grains were tossed in the air. The husks blew away in the wind.

Finally, Peter's family was ready to cook the rice grains. This was the easiest part.

That night, the family ate the wonderful wild rice from the harvest. As they ate, Grandfather told them the story of the great hero Manabozho.

Grandfather began, "Many years ago, Manabozho's people had no food during the cold winters. Then one night, Manabozho had a dream. He dreamed that he saw dancers near a lake. He danced with them. When he woke up, he saw that the dancers were really the wild grasses. He saw the birds eat the grass seeds. Manabozho told his people the good news. There was an abundance of food to eat all around them in the lake. That was the first harvest."

Peter looked at the food on the table. He smiled and finished eating the delicious *manoomin*.